'Part atmospheric folk story, part lyrical poem, Natasha Carthew's gritty, cir  and tales of female inger ttable.' Josephine Corcoran

'Brutal and tender,
beautiful tale of fen
through the genera   ldlife
Writer

'The story of working class history wasn't fastened in books, it was written in the landscape, in the weather, in voices carried on the wind. These stories are an excavation of that storm of lost voices, but you'll find no sentimental reminiscence here, nor a report of victimhood. What Carthew offers is the raw recognition of an identity and culture hewn from hard work. These stories comes rushing out from the land with the power of that voice that refuses silence as a soaring, mythic anthem.' Carmen Marcus - Writer

'Natasha Carthew's prose-poem plunges into the darkness of Cornwall's past and the uncertainties of its future. Ancestors, folkloric creatures, sombre mine-depths, turbulent seas, despair and hope: all are melded in an unforgettably powerful evocation of Cornwall's heritage, its landscapes and people.' Prof Carolyne Larrington - Professor of Medieval European Literature, University of Oxford

'An important book, using language hewn from the author's deep and intimate knowledge of a time and place; a successful literary and artistic reimagining.' Karen Lloyd - award winning Writer and Environmental Activist

'Natasha Carthew's characters seem to grow and tumble like cliff fauna out of the briny Cornish seascapes from which they were imagined. Reading these stories, one can

almost assume the magnetic prose and poetry has been channelled rather than designed — that only Carthew, with her intimate connection to nature and to the region, could have produced such a unique, beautiful piece of writing.'
Sarah Leipciger - Author

BORN BETWEEN CROSSES

an exploration of rural working women

by
Natasha Carthew

First published April 2021 by Hypatia Publications

Natasha Carthew has asserted her right to be identified as author of this work

© Natasha Carthew, 2021

ISBN (paperback): 978-1-872229-71-3
ISBN (eBook): 978-1-872229-72-0

Layout and typeset in Palatino Linotype and Segoe Print in-house by Linda Cleary at Hypatia Publications

Printed in Great Britain at Headland Printers, Cornwall on FSC accredited paper stocks. Chemical free digital printing process, from an environmentally friendly run factory.

Hypatia Publications
imprint of
The Hypatia Trust
Penzance Cornwall
www.hypatia-trust.org.uk

CONTENTS

*For my mother, who taught me to not only survive
but thrive.*

INTRODUCTION

The idea for *Born Between Crosses* has been with me for the longest time, perhaps before memory made itself known. As a young girl I remember watching as my mother prepared for another shift as chambermaid at the local hotel whilst juggling many other cleaning jobs for the private homes, holiday homes and the local pub in our village in Cornwall in order to keep a roof over our heads, clothes on our backs and food on the table. Growing up my mother was a survivalist, she had no choice, and it was the same for my grandmother who up until her death worked as a cleaner for the Duke of Somerset.

Most recently I realised this collection would not just be an assembly of anecdotes, poems and stories, but a combination of all three; some of these are my stories, some of them are yours, but together they are our collected history.

These interconnecting prose-poems explore the challenges that face rural working class women; the long tedious hours, the minimum wage and the lack of opportunity. More than anything, it's the lack of recognition; but *Born Between Crosses* is set to change that.

Natasha Carthew
Author

All good stories start with the mother
your mother
I am
whatever you think
when you think about her

a pool of soothing water
in summer

the crocheted scarf and gloves
in winter

I am
what you feel
when you feel her

there
and here
take this

I have lived 4.54 billion years
fifth element
infinite space
my luminescence dances like dew on the first blades
of grass
and on the leaves of insignificant trees
to become you
a glint in your father's eye
I've had them all
soldier
sailor
bin man

thief
Not made of sugar or spice
I am the wind in your hair
the blood between your legs
I am the sweat that comes from working
graveyards and double shifts
menopausal
I am a lifetime at drift

All great stories start and end with the mother
I am
the book that sits on your lap at bedtime
the hug that says
we're okay
look
I'll add another job to the rest
Early mornings late nights
but my sweet child this will work out right
I'll find a way
make it work
hey
look at me
my hip to the grindstone
I'll keep at it

Celebrate

All our stories
for eternity
I have collected up
if you look
between the crosses
of burden
dig your nails into the dirt

to find the roots of your foundation
where you start
together
we are
history

All good women have stories
trust me
in the heat of a twelve hour factory shift
the weight of wings
and the lift of dirty water

I've seen it
the freezing washday wind
and everything so fucking backbreaking
brutal

and yet

your words
my words
whatever you imagine as beautiful
I am
you
me
together we are the start
and the end
and the beginning of everything

No matter what load you have to bear
remember
I am your mother
nature
and the gift I give to you

are not the crosses
of endurance or birth
but two lines passing
mere kisses
etched in love

1

THE WEIGHT OF SUMMER AS WATER

The Palm of her Hand
Swim
The Weight of These Wings
River Running Over

The Palm Of Her Hand

Rain in
the summer heat breaks

the line between the past
present
future

wakes

something in the way we see ourselves
in the stories of our ancestors

no longer words
but it's all in the eyes of our elders

sounds of not just what we're told
but what we know

Grandmother

Thunder
the young girl lowers the old women into the bath and
watches as she floats
sheet lightning
a feather adrift
barely visible
this

silver shadow slipping
beneath the tideline

a good life pulling away
in handfuls
the memory of hardship
and the laughter

no matter

Did you see the photo of me working at the harbourside?
Your mum has it somewhere

Pride of place
mantelpiece

pushing the objects and trinkets like lobster pots
come to life

you wouldn't think it
look at me now

the young girl smiles
beautiful
lifts the water
washes her

fine fillet features and skin as soft as sea beech
pink as pretty
white in the bone

her hands still dyed with a hundred Cornish summers
drift-seed brown

come from the ground
like rocks forged at the docks

holding all the secrets of a long life
tough as fuck

in those two hands
the creases and the cracks
cross
her destiny laid bare
where her long life scratched into the fine line

detail
of a hardship
incomprehensible

some say
how hard
women's work

but it's written in the palm
of this woman's hand
raised to work
knee-high to the fish-factory floor

brow beaten in concentration
the traffic of crabs, mackerel, pilchards
that never stayed long

in their place
destined for the table, the city
settings the likes of them would never see

she
takes both hands and puts a thumb into each one
two clams
pushing until she feels the essence

of this grand woman

heartbeat building
as they unfurl
and wash away the grey

sand

two pearls
a gift each
grandmother says

one for you
and one for your mum

to remember

the best of what we have
we know
is closest to home

our blood
you'll understand when you reach up
working age

join your mother
and our ancestors
together
bound
within the harbourside wall

Swim

Knife goes in

the woman with the bill worry
food and rent money
school trips for the kids
respite care for her mum
slips the blade beneath the skin

heaven
a deep dive until the water no longer exists
out there

but lives within
and she starts to swim

beyond the factory floor
the damp wall slipping into rock pools
the quay the nets and pots and ropes
floating hope
like someone else's dream

moving water
from the sluice to the river
the estuary into the ocean
the woman with the salt of the earth
in her hair
beneath her nails
finally gives herself over to the motion
of letting go

her raw-red fingers becoming fins

her ears like gills listening
the sound of the knife
gutting
bills to pay
roof to keep
but beneath the waves she is free a minute

work away
swimming

The Weight Of These Wings

Summer slips by like a slow-blow punch to the head
the stench of seaweed dug in on a high wind
the sound of rich kids playing out on the rocks
too early
the woman looks at the kitchen clock
stopped

She stands
hands cupped beneath the constant drip
a bit for drinking
splashing
some thing to buy a little alone time
to abide
thinking
how to put the day away

Backalong she used to give herself a day off
just that
a day away from drudgery
dread
take herself away from the trailer
and plan for her future
make lists
mental
the 'where I want to be in three years'

she'd picture it

sketchpad
good paints
a view apart from the tourists

posh campsites and second home-owners

they didn't like her
whatever
knew what she did cus who didn't?

Family business
burden

the dusk
and the dawn
and the space between that came fingering through the
bracken
ghost knocking in the dark
the night spread out like an open invite

Welcoming bed

and the noise
the silence

Some night pain
and the days that followed
her future suddenly flush with absent thought
and the art she knew she would never sell

Oh well

They asked for seascapes in the village gallery
only wanted to sell the pretty picture
ripped roses around the door
the cloudless sky when round their way it mostly rained
over and over again

the days painted with another blow
bruise blue
the heart of her home beautiful
but hopelessly so
there were things that hid
behind hammered doors
and fell between the poky pasty shops
each and every tourist knew the name for it
the thing they mistook for misery

Poverty
loaded gun

The mizzle made a mess of any kind of clear view
made it hard to call it by its name
but still
she had a plan
a future bulleted to the kitchen wall
points that meant freedom
not fear

the wives pulling at their kids word in your ear
no time for flight
the husbands sniffing out come midnight

common thought was she should not be here
despite her heritage
family name
if they bothered to listen she would have told them

she too held onto dreams
like a string of pearls
she used to count them out
as a kid

before she knew that pretty things could be fake

fucked
stopped clock

She stands at the sink
adjusts her hair
bit of lippy applied to her reflection
no art tonight
just the long dusk light
drawn out
wet around its ears with mist and the ocean adrift

oblivious to all this
few years
she says

picture it
tomorrow
some dream to hold

a stranger's shadow on the front porch
she folds her wings
a neat trick
and tucks them beneath the sink

River Running Over

Commissioned by Literature Works and the Canal & River Trust

All week they stood and stared into the abyss. Forgetful,
trying to remember something scratch at their heads until
they found a scab to pick and something fell loose; the right
idea the right thought the one that made the most sense said
here, somewhere here is what we miss.

I see this
from where I drift
my good eye milky but moving
gone over with slow filmic shutter speed
plastic bags the new world seaweed
I see things differently now
oil on something
what was it?

Each day they crept up the same way hands and paws
patting the ground feeling around for the unfamiliar press
of a puddle, their tongues thick with the shit and grit of
question after question, they didn't get it.

What had they done when they knew what well what could
they do?

They asked this often some days when spit allowed they
shouted it, nothing was the answer, it was nearly over.
I told them this despite my thick lip split from the battle of
hit and miss.

I am drunk but not the good kind, too many times punched
they finally did what I knew they would, I'm down, zero to
the ground, almost out.

All week, every week every month and year each decade I
have lost time to that ticking bomb, no matter how I clear
my head of fag-ends and the lids of Costa Coffee cups try to
remember the boats and the bustle, the rope and the rigging
and the trade coming in on a spring wind, I miss the swim
of things.

Sometimes I hear them talk about the seasons, words
trickling into my good ear where the tar is not so thick they
say how they miss the winter storms how they hated the
floods but despise this neat heat more.

I agree.

Once I tried to show them
I shrank drop down into something manageable
something they could use, could carry
at first I thought they loved me
took me home in buckets to covet
they brought me into their lives like I was the eighth
wonder

Turns out I am
close to gone.
I have some memory of what was said; sink, toilet, kettle,
pathogens, flower bed.

Yesterday I learnt a new word shouted out from kids
sticking a dog dead-centre in my belly, the word was
drought.
It made me shake despite the heat meandering muscle
memory had me lose myself, few drops left.

Remembrance returned and put upon the quayside the men
in their rough handled hats and the women in their heavy

skirts hitching up against my banks I learnt the words like
they were my words

Carding
Spinning
Kersey
Serge
Long wool
Fleece

One summer I met a deaf girl who worked the mill used to
talk when she thought no one was listening - I was, always.
Feet catching the drift of me head in the clouds, she'd
lost her hearing at the shuttle side me my sense of touch
together we sat and looked up at the sky made memories of
the anvil clouds wished upon the same occasional rainbow

Beautiful
colourful
water in
water out
like breath it ripped the heavens open

now nothing
sky baited
everybody waiting
tragic.

Today I woke in the knowledge that this would be my last
day, could feel it in the way my skin peeled revealed the
bones that had contained me more rust than rock, the earth
that had stayed with me all these years was crumbling,
folding, packing up and going home, so long

Years

months
days down to a fine trickle

If this is it
if this is all there is
I have come to realise
one thing
they will miss me more than I could ever miss them
their thirst for how things used to be will make me smile
from beyond my refraction
my laugh drawn out in perfect fine arc lines
running
no tears no water to cry
the death of them will be shocking
but worth it
and the tragedy of what they knew as water
river
will be over.

Summer passes
and I look to breathe
again
leaving the water and the coastal villages
trashed and strewn like an unmade bed
the cans and condoms
polystyrene body-boards
and the tiny pretty cylinders of nitrous oxide
laughing gas but I find nothing funny

The teenage girls with their broke hearts and
bloody sheets
and the seasonal workers back to wandering the
autumnal streets
zero hours and the long road barrel of a shotgun
I leave them the last of the hedges
lipstick fruit as sweet as anything to help them

I hope

My nature is as protector
but I feel the season turn as quick
as the tourists finding their feet
remembering
first homes and good jobs

I too am moving on
my earthen heart turned toward town
a mother checking in on her brood
so I might leave a little found light

the remnant of a star hidden within unexpected
margins

and all its corners intact
kiss kiss

a gift for you so you might remember
like words in a newly discovered book

a guide on how to live
to love
how you might learn to hope

2

THE HEART OF AUTUMN AS EARTH

Library Book
Water Music
Mother Bird

Library Book

At the back of the closed down library
there is a book
that slipped
between the trestle tables
of the sale that said
everything must go

the stories
of the women
who worked the mines
backalong
and forward
toward a better life
in time

perhaps
for the kids and their kids' kids
the bal-maidens who smashed the luck
out of the rocks in storm weather
together
they stand
frocks and gooks and frowns that they will pass down

the photos
that you might never see
and the names that you might never know
but still
everything begins with a shift

seismic or butterfly
and that is why

there is a story
in a book
fallen
at the back of the closed down library

Water Music

Water in
Water out.

The young woman tells herself to remember the sea, the
way the tide sinks the sand down to rock pools without
notice. A memory of home from before the move to town
for some job, little money.

Water into the bucket,
half decent cloth,
rinse it,
does for everything so she's been told but she's not stupid,
a cleaner knows the difference
knows the mop absorbs piss in one room, puts it down in
another.

She's been working in the nursing home for two years,
she reckons so, was only meant for one year and yet
here she is, her life dug mud deep into her third, strange
how something so hot-heavy and uncomfortable as
responsibility can land legs up in your lap without noticing.

At home on the coast autumn meant back to school, the wait
at the end of the lane, twenty miles on the bus, round trip,
a season come in with the slow inching of the hay in fields
still pink with thinking; but the inland town she has found
herself is unmoving, holds the early frost in its dead red
bricks, fumbles with time until it has all clocks stopped.

Two years of constant inch grey water enough to darken
the linoleum in case Matron comes poking, looking for an
excuse to hold her back it takes everything to make sure she
about turns, says good job, secure an extra quid in Friday's

brown envelope.

Takes ten minutes to clean a room, longer if you catch it looking, old dears thirty in all and each and every one of them caught hedge-ways, going somewhere or coming from, the briar of dementia scrambled in their hair, their eyes, pinching on the tip of their tongue.

A couple still knew their own names, some knew the girl was not their granddaughter, grandson, but no matter the length of fence they were all still trapped; thoughts, high-chair seats and high-sided baths, shouting for the teenager to cut their throat or help get them the fuck out.

Help.

Water in
Water out.

At the basin she mists a little spray to catch the sun, add sparkle, watches an older nurse pull down the sheets, the nightdress pushed up to the neck she nudges past her to wet the sponge.
How long?
Piece of string.
How long is that?
Forever.
She looks at the girl and tells her to not get stuck in this rubble rut, find other interests.
The girl tells her she does, says something about words, being a writer, this makes the woman laugh, stupid kid, we're working class.

In the mirror she can see the old woman crying, silent, the water on her flimsy thin skin hurts, she says.

Not long now.
Think of better things.
The girl knows the old woman has good thoughts,
memories as big as a heatwave, some days she can hear
them reel in like thunder, but not today, the eyes are closed,
this will be her last autumn, she knows

Silent tears

shed because she can no longer recall the landmarks of
childhood, the steeple and the cross of the Methodist church
up on the hill or the field behind the cattle mart where she
used to play as a kid, she can sense her youth suffocated by
a car park, a black bird running, shouting.

The girl dries her hands.

Some days she notices the wire, feels the edge of the fence,
once she bumped straight into it, said there were worse
things to do than talk to old folk, she hated cleaning but
loved their embroidered glory stories;

Washer Woman
Workhouse Scum
Chambermaid
Scullery Maid
Fishwife
Housewife
Factory Worker
Mother

One old dear always called her Peter, said she was her lover,
another used to cry for her father to stop, please God, it hurt.
Another taught her the names of all the early autumn
flowers in the garden, with her tongue she bowed them up

into an impossibly pretty posy

Dahlia
Celosia
Aster

The girl kept them at the back of her mind, threaded them
into a tiny jam-jar with a little found water, what she could
afford at the time.

Water in
Water out.

How many plastic jugs and beakers of liquid never got
drunk? Every room on every level of the faded town house
had them tipped across the tiny tables or punched across
the floor. Nobody knew there was a price on their heads,
but if they did they wouldn't have cared, each and every
one of them had survived the war, the worst of times, the
moments of lucidity when memory washed clear they
would tell the girl it was the best years of their lives.

They got to dig ditches, drive trucks, chop trees for posts to
prop up the trenches and make deliveries across the country
on their time, drink ale, eat regional pies, have a lad to fuck
in every port.

These the women who worked and loved and lived the
same as any, drank their share and spilt blood, their
relationship with liquid was rough, rocky, but compared
to this, so much easier, their lives soaked through the
unforgiving earth with hope and good God glory.

Drink this.
Let us wash that.

One nurse liked to shame them; dirty bitch, you've pissed
your pants.

Some days the girl caught them looking.
Moments of being when she wanted to tell them that she
loved them, ask what could be done to help more than
water to drink, water to wash away, show them an old
photo from off the sideboard, blow the dust, wedding day.

If the girl could have found somewhere to put all the
fragments of their memories she would have, just that, but
it was hard enough to catch their words, trap thin air, even
harder to collect recollection, slippery like water, harder in
the run up to winter, dumb teenager.

If she knew how to peel each sentence from them and press
into a story, some way to honour their fuck-hard hands and
soft hearts into a tome of glory, remember this

life made easier
for them
herself
for all the women
and the girls to come

If only she could put the water in
time taken, given
and swim
through history
turn the tide
and take their stories
like a thousand cool glasses of water
words to gather up like broken bricks
make something of it
If she could build a wall to sit upon

make a monument to their lives
that through history
had been omitted

listen in to their whispered words
washing in, like water
music.

Mother Bird

7.00
again
a bird on the wing scoops down, starts to walk
weaving her way toward work
first light.

Beneath her feet the first of the leaves catch in her claws
cling to the hem of her hand-me-down tail
skirts of brown feathers gone black in the damn dark light
early bird
worms for the kids
catching cold but keep it a secret.

7.01
The day over before it's begun
Bird crosses the market square and feathers her keys
takes her time to find a thread better than
yesterday
today
tomorrow
still here
something shiny in memory to catch her eye
own childhood
the shape and solace of her parents' nest
plume poor but protected
well fed
love was always four clipped wings
circling.

Good days
she says

she hopes her children will remember this
the way she remembered that
love came in many pieces
meal
after meal
no matter how small
generations of black birds
living claw to beak
hand to tight gripped lips.

7.08
Bird realises that she's late
through the caged window
pawn shop
she can see the hands of the clock
giving her the Vs
tick bloody tock
she puts the key into the door
unlocks
disables the alarm with the tip of her good wing
pecks the strobe light bright
welcoming.

7.09
she turns the sign
smiles
good prices paid for your silver, your gold
few pennies for anything old
memories
stolen goods
ding ding

a junkie gull kid jumps forward
same as always

sad smile
yellow red-rimmed eyes
blinking lies
come in.

Bird watches from her perch behind the counter
helps herself to a few found seeds
drop of water
listens whilst the girl tells her she's just here to look
around the tiny box room
Bird thinks how it always starts like this
with a clearing of the throat
small found words
got this unwanted gift.

Carrier bag
was from me dad
the girl in the grey cap turns her head
few bottle tops
toffee wrappers
says she's no kid
no time for playing dress up
says she's destined for bigger things
clouds and stars and then some
so, she coughs
how much?

7.30
Bird can hear the cockerel in next door's unit shout
still early
says she's not in the market
tight, like
truth is she's good at sniffing
her beak as small as a golden darning needle, but still

she watches the ten o'clock news
reads the local paper when it blows up onto the porch
the county-line gangs
don't just steal the tourists' fish and chips
but pick their unsuspecting pockets
small town kids
she wonders
how did it come to this?

Bird swallows hard
clears her throat
sings a friendly tune that ends with the thought of her own
brood
mouths to feed
the need for dreams
bills to pay
despite the look in the girl gull's eye

the whisper of please, I need it
couple wraps
should do it

Gull ruffles some feathers, her own
and that's when Bird sees it
a knife so big and bright she knows to leave this

8.00
out of pocket
again
Bird knows she'll work this shift until dusk
or death
a job to hold down
keep
another twelve hour shift

until the night drifts closer

Bird on the wind
takes flight
the kids to feed and back to bed
no worry
tomorrow's another day
and tonight she'll go hungry
again.

*O*f all the windows I peer into
all the doors I cherry-knock
quick look
no matter how I try to help
the best part of me left
the flawless auburn sedum
late raspberry fruit
a sunset
on your doorstep
gifts to lift the spirit
of those who do not think of me

fifth element
I am the space
between
your fingers and the earth
when you dig
the light within
the moor's horizon
when you look
for me

I am
the warm wind despite winter's creep
the gap in the hedge
that sits
between the rocks the tors
and the hardest place
that you might ever face

an unopened window
curtains closed but still
I pass to you

the best part of truth

memory
history
community
is your identity.

3

THE BURDEN OF WINTER AS FIRE

Just a Girl
Object
The Hand That Feeds

Just a Girl

The moors in winter was no place for a thinker
she said
just a girl with dreams that stretched further
than heaven

the boggy earth beneath her feet
the granite bone
that weighed her down
sitting out on the crossroads
not a child but still
no movement more than not quite grown

small thing
her age irrelevant
always the last to be put to task
just a girl surplus to the world
set straight on some distant path
and in her head

the wonder that was in her
sorting the wheat from the chaff
unquenchable fire
like a thirst
those that were happy to live out their lives on the moor
and those who would not

no place for a dreamer
she was
the insignificant girl with the perception set in
the task of any book
any page

to read to write to imagine
more than the stubborn horizon

backcountry at her age was no place for rage
her anger at the injustice of so many things
old ways
the women cooking cleaning rearing, pin-money
and the men with their one dimension, just work

the heath was no safe place
for big dreams
small thinking
it crept in
three colours
black night
bright summer
and the grey shade of winter

the indifferent sky
and the tors with their heads in the clouds
low and oblivious
to the burden of decision

made
the young woman with dreams in her own hands
coach ticket
and the letter that read
acceptance

small thing
but to a girl who had nothing
her fate was sacred
like a relic dug out from heritage earth

the gift of study
and the wilderness of some unknown city
flashing neon
and the lights up close
that turn
toward

just a girl
standing in the road
sticks out her thumb
remembers to leave a little of herself in the ground
a navigational compass
so she might return
her home, her heart
but not right now.

Object

object sits
waits
the sticky side of the bar her prop
deep breath

inhale
fag between her lips
looks up
glitter ball above her head

object smiles at her reflection
a clown juggling the optics

still got it if you squint a bit
it's all in the wink
slide of tongue
lipstick

object waits for the door to swing
7 p.m. and the regular blokes

demand their usual
cheap pints
the exotic object is out of their league
they know
but still they ask
what country you from

Cornwall born and raised

they laugh
ask for more cleavage

please
feeling flush
keep the change
your type of women relies on tips
poor bitch

ask what culture and she replies
not this
punch-drunk banter
what time might grant her
salvation
midnight
whatever came first
to disrupt
the start of the monthly country disco
spring suddenly in sight

object listens in on their discussion
like a mission
where to put her
she's in their hands
putty
put pretty on the shelf
they say

good game
easy lay
think object has lost her hearing
no ears despite the mad mandatory earrings

listen

if only they knew
that she was one of two workings

where one arm started
another's ended
at home in bed

mended the cracks with gilt and superglue
not so fragile
their patterns alone looked incomplete
but object knew

how delicate
how powerful

two women together
could be
circular
soaring
happy

loving

settling in on a job
by definition
did not define

object knew
her mind her own

something pretty to look at
the cross around her neck that meant eternal life
and fuck off was a gift from my wife

making money the good graft way
with salt lifted and carried from the stubborn earth

no glitz
no glamour in lack of opportunity
for what it wasn't worth

object serves and sits
to live out her life in poverty
a little dust catching in her hair
occasionally

a diamond in the rough
they say
she says
not so much

back to the wall
she switches the light
the slow creak turn of the glitter ball
the bar on the moor opens
like a gutter
but object knows it doesn't matter
from her shelf she rises
higher

it's just work
and anyway
has other things to think about besides
head in the smoky clouds
she belongs to the midwinter stars.

The Hand That Feeds

Wind backs around
comes down from the north ground
feeds the air with freezing cold
but underneath clear skies at least
we know the sun will rise

Against unforgiving horizons
steel from ancient industry
riding the skyline in near memory movement
a heard of relative's name
but a stranger's face all the same

Winter's work is this and that
strong arms encircling heavy weights
legs to hike as far as daylight
beyond
a bit of piecemeal
two towns over
past the county line

The hand that feeds
dry and cracked with the digging
like spades
the mouths that mark the table
baby birds
each with a different song
sung and then forgotten

Wind backs around and will back down
silence the cries
eventually

will force feed the air with a little hope
crossed fingers and crossed toes
small steps to the sunrise.

All good stories end
with the passing of another season
the reason for the early up
late to bed
winter ends the year harsh
starts worse

I see it in the way the meals are made
how the clothes for the kids get stitched, re-
patched
worked into flowers, butterflies, patterns to
pretend

something as new

as a pin
or a tree
I see
little light
windows loose and damp wood
the warmth of a fire
losing its grip
exiting through the single glaze
my branches like fingers
reach and grab for the heat
and turn it
push it down into my root boots
good to go
to leave

the worst of times behind
some say
the best is yet to come

the promise of things budding, hidden
the snowdrops that grace the garden
relieving the burden
with all good stories
hope
a way to believe
that somehow you will be able to see the woods
for the trees

my daughters I promise
I am here
leaves listening

one word whispers
are your words
my thoughts
exhaled
and exchanged
secretly
through the silent keyhole
each cross you bear
I lift and bury into the ground
the fields and the farms

no sound
but the wind against your cheek
the distant ocean bullying the cliff's split lip
the river running

and you
each and every one
my daughter
whatever you think
I am

you
me
together we are formidable
the foundation of something
where we might build brilliance

a moment's kiss
one minute's belief to seal this
not what we lack
but all the strength and intelligence we've got

the legacy of us working class
women
is not the start
or the end
but everything.

4

THE KISS OF SPRING AS AIR

The Crimson Seed
Dig
Hope's Heart Beats

The Crimson Seed

A run of parsnips laid crossways to the table, babies not long born and old men boxed ready for the grave. The old woman fingered the mud blood from their faces and plucked at the tassel hairs and she told them they were fine looking boys for the time of year despite being buggers to pick from the frozen earth.

Behind her on the bit-and-bang dresser sat the folded letter. She read it out loud from memory and chewed the words roundabout in her mouth like a big bite of happy food. She went to the calendar bought special for the occasion and tapped a mud print on today's date and nodded. It was about time, a long time coming.

She bent to the wood burner and fed it last winter's fall and stretched a little of what was left of life into her cold-snap bones. Eighty plus years pressed hard into the lean farm fabric and yet time had moved so fast it was as if it hadn't moved at all.

Every day sketched in similar ink both hope and disappointment lying side by side, saying tomorrow maybe and then tomorrow maybe the next and the next. Some days living alone on the farm had her crazed, but mostly it gave her purpose, kept her eyes above level ground, her head from out the trenches.

She put a pan of water to the hot plate stove made herself a mug of coffee and carried it out onto the porch to drink. The desolate farmland was like a mist muddle of tangled sheets and the white of night snow grabbed too close to the cabin. "Typical!" she snapped. "One time got a visitor comin' and snow is what we get." She stood at the good bit of rail that didn't threaten so much and looked toward the horizon, distant land, the place where all things started, where they ended as things turned out.

Today somebody was paying her a visit, a long time coming they were returning home to her.

"Comrade," she said, "why did it have to take this long?" She set the mug down on the rail and kept a finger to it for the warmth, narrowed her eyes to the skyline for unusual shadow but saw nothing, just the side swiped trees yammering in the wind.

She closed her eyes and remembered similar trees, their shadows overlooking a thousand trampling war-worn feet found her memory returned and sitting with the one boy her only friend at her side.

The smell of decay came to her and cascaded in a waterway rush, she could taste it fizzle on her tongue, felt the bile push against her chest and her throat enter her mouth.

Got a ciggie?
Boy, dive blue eyes
says No
kicks his boots out into the mud, says
Now you got me
thinking things
the comfort of home

Sorry

She didn't mean to rope and pull in that other life
wanted to talk for the sake of words
familiarity in typical talk

besides
the others never spoke
young men with their mothers on their minds

mostly

She sat back
wiggled her head which-way until it settled for something
the divot between two ridges
bridge in the mud bank
tried to forget the itch of her shaved head
the sentiment that went with long hair
the thing she missed

Drink?
Fucksake Jo
He made her laugh
Fucksake lad

Smile
secret disguise
her greatest delight
how he looked at her
something sacred
brother in arms

if only

Some whiskey
she held out her hands, took the hipflask
wrapped her fingers around
something to know in a place
where there was nothing but horror
to hold

nothing to make sense
no way to familiarise themselves
with this
landscape
shot through
and the crimson sky infiltrating
through gaps
the makeshift crosses
the bombed out church
the wind-caught bell that never ended in this

near miss glow of candlelight
minds adrift with fear
one wish
and the flash of occasional stars
watching over two soldiers
keeping face
not falling in love

Jo opened her eyes and blinked at the bright clean snow, remembering a young woman whose only crime was to want something more than what her sex dictated. She flinched at the thought of missed opportunities, a life spent mostly in disguise; she'd wanted to fight in the war fight for her country, that was all.

She took a gulp of coffee and splashed the rest into a melting hollow in the early spring snow, "S'pose I should visit the stock, see 'em new-borns int dead yet."

She resigned herself to the slow pull of wellies and wrap of good thick coat and she stepped from the cabin into the snow, buttoning and upping her collar as she edged toward the barn.

Winter had been rough in recent years; the snow came earlier each autumn and settled into spring like estranged kin, the days too cold and short and the nights too much of a bad thing, her whole life waiting for something that someone to come.

A friend, a lover before love had a chance to begin; she had been an optimistic girl back then, optimistic and foolish, she had wanted him to forgive her fall for her the way he was supposed. A girl returned from battle same as him, there was no shame in sharing what they'd been through, what they could become.

She stabbed her fists into her pockets and went on down the track toward the barn. There was a strong wind blowing in from the north, a strong wind that made it a day for battening down, a day not meant for visitors and premature lambs. She could hear them call through the rattling clapboard walls as she approached, could hear their tiny screams stretch and snap like cheap twine thinned and tied too tight.

"I'm comin'!" she shouted. "Like bloody babies," she worked the latch on the door and stood against the doorframe waited for her eyes to unpin themselves from the shock of an all-white landscape.

The barn was nothing more than four miracle walls and a roof heavy enough to keep them from toppling, not much space for anything but the cow that gave occasional milk and the sheep that spat their babies too early or too late onto the straw no matter what day of the year the ram paid visit. This year they'd decided on too early and this, coupled with the lateness of winter, was all that was needed for a little more than necessary disaster.

The half dozen ewes sat together in a coven and they eyed their lambs with apathy. "Dint ask you to born 'em in winter," said Jo, "dint ask you for nothin' but what you was s'posed." She went to the lambs and counted them out and the one apart she knelt beside and pulled it into her lap, careful to keep it calm whilst some sorry soldier song rattled and drummed in her head, her heart.

The battlefield closed around.

Thick drifts of trampled earth
kicked shit with the fighting still in it

sunk

the foreign land and
grave upon grave
giving way

for the lucky ones
edging into daylight

body parts and broken hearts
weeping
winking
as surprised as the sun.

It was a job to heave
what they couldn't name
from the suck

she and the boys
wet around kids
picking and gathering

like back home
the spuds in the fields

they were the lucky ones
was what they were told
but there was no good fortune
in breaking

apart
they all knew

this was duty
was all

heart beating
it wasn't enough
but
sudden surprise
the same way she hadn't reckoned on

falling

They gave the boy morphine
carried him between them
legs exploded
blood scattered like crimson seed
said all alright
despite
stupid words snagging on the ice-peaked mud like bunting at a
wake
ridiculous

They held the dying boy
shared him until he gave up on life

held each other long into the night
love for the first time
and everything laid out
existence and expiry gathered in momentary memory
like a song never before sung
but suddenly known

The lyrics came back to her like a slap and she sung them out into both worlds like they were the only words she knew and she carried the lamb back to the cabin on the music of that terrible, beautiful marching song.

She returned to the kitchen and circled a stack of hessian sacks before the fire and laid the lamb like a God-offering within and she went to the pantry for the last bit of milk and ran it into the teat bottle.

The storm was in or close to it and it stabbed its tongue beneath the badly hung doors and spat at the windows to let it in.

People would talk about this winter for years to come, mark it as the worst in living memory and chalk it up like a benchmark to misery. Jo didn't care, knew her light was dimming day by day; a storm was nothing but a storm to her now, another mountain in a ridge of mountains to negotiate, to climb.

She warmed the milk a little within the clutch of both hands and sat with the teat on its gums and told it this was the time to decide whether to live or die.

Outside on the porch she could hear the dog bark more than the simple call for warmth and shelter he was telling her something. "Comin'!" She nestled the bottle toward the lamb and pulled herself to her feet.

The day had gotten tangled up with the storm and the dying lamb and she wondered if her visitor would make it up the track at all. She opened the door and felt the dog run behind her legs, one step from swearing one step from keeling over and that was when she saw it; a lonely black vehicle crawling like a stone throw in the snow, a long lost something idling, black against white, a cut out torn from an old world and pasted into the new.

Jo stepped from the porch and crossed the field to stand out on the white-wash trail, she had been waiting for this moment seventy years, reminding herself that what she knew of death was in the present - it wasn't a bad thing, just a thing was all.

A bag of bones burnt and boxed and a soldier's dying wish to come home to her, after all these years a memory of first love in another time and place.

Jo thanked the driver and signed the form. Carried the box with the rough cross etched on its lid and placed it beside the parsnips on the table.

"Our visitor's arrived." She looked at the dog but he wasn't listening, his head turned toward the lamb; the red of birth blood split about its mouth and the flag white milk finally found, a new life budding, a crimson seed, flowering. Peace at last.

Dig

Dig
put your back into it

I do

Out in the fields I can be
whoever I want to be

wild fire
flame
sickly sweet sixteen
not yet a woman
but not quite a girl

born on the cusp of what it is to be
and what it's like to look

at the way the boys do things
without thinking
and I am like them

all sweat and heat
I know

I dig
beneath the everyday work clothes
to find my skin
the zip that circles below
Adam's rib
I peel it back in the hope that it might reveal
something

where the tough flint starts
and sparks

hints at why I stand out
a needle in the red-hot hay stack
why I'm not quite right

farm strong
wrong
could do myself a favour
they say
tone myself down
don't talk so loud
walk so fast

can't change the past
but the future is set
squared
running between the kitchen table
subservient
and the village chapel

accept this

country girls don't have no destiny but
what you can see
binary
they say

take a look at the neighbour's son
his farm
cus this land won't go to you
your future is set in another's mud and grit
shovel it and burn it all you want

either way

dig
down into the ground
my back breaks
but
it keeps the fire in my belly in place
the winter of youth is behind me
spring pissing in on the air
promises
another place

my heart is here but I am the season turned
what I was born
what I'm becoming
neither the deer or the doe that crosses our land
I am both things
I am a new thing
out in the fields
I can see my future
spring rising
worshipping

Sixteen
and my bags already packed

I look back at the farmhouse
one final time

and dig.

Hope's Heart Beats

Mother Nature's story

Commissioned by the National Trust to mark the first day of spring 2020

The sweetest part of dawn is the silence before the chorus, the moment after; the song thrush and the blackbird first up and then the great tits and the sparrows all asking, where is the sun? They build their nests with their eyes on the horizon soften the twigs with egg-safe star stitched moss and the pull of lamb's wool plucked fresh from the barb they spin it with the hope of golden thread, good yarn. Gaia sits at her window and looks out beyond the communal garden waits for the light to reveal itself its fingers running through the drying remains of last year's harvest, the ribbons of greenery chasing the hill through the wasteland and down toward the forest.

If she stands on her flowerbed she can see the needling floor the carpet of wood anemone and the curls of wild scent garlic, sees the eyes of a tiny deer his fresh infant antlers gleaming as he steps across the treeline into path blockers, shin catchers, he calls out, hear this.

All the world is reciting a prayer. Gaia puts her ear to the mud wall to catch the jackdaw chatter next door the husband saying today is the day spring equinox after all but the wife won't have any of it, not until she sees her first butterfly, Brimstone, got to be.

Beneath the girl's feet down the tree a bit, Mum is in the kitchen reciting her poem, the one that rumbles on about the turn of the Earth, her heart pining for the lengthening of the light, but Gaia knows despite her young age that the rain was still in at night she heard the drumroll thud of every winter word stamped out amongst the marsh marigolds, the ones that circled the flats their glow like stepping stones between the patches of foot pooled mud.

In the bathroom she hears her siblings sing today's the day that the earth commences its tilt the pull of the Sun from its root, his gift of love and heat to everyone, they said it was true, a Mum promise, pinky. She could hear them splash in the organic mineral matter moving like dippers in the bath, their hands playing beneath the plank that was meant for soap but instead held up a sign that shouted 'Do not move, frog path.'

The scent of blackthorn and Gaia took a step toward her door the sight of gorse grass on the landing caught her smiling, the lichen with its new colour and the magnolia swinging on the open door breeze, chandelier, candles calling her telling her to go on find the Sun and bring him home.

Down the petal staircase and across the landing made of Lenten roses, the young girl snuck into the kitchen grabbed the cosy straight off the pot something warm to wear until the Sun finally decided to get up.

Outside their flat time tasted a little less predictable stretched out with the dark chew of deadened grass and nettle stems salted by winter, the sky unsure of itself and the clouds that lingered in its breadth, hammered with anxious thoughts the girl held up her hands made a wish on a dandelion, big blow promise, "I'll find you."

She made tracks through the garden and traced the celandine path out past the skeletal washing lines that pegged in colourful buds, her ear pinned to more than the usual movement the roads and railways that had silenced in recent days to make space for the cry of a buzzard and the hawk of chiff-chaffs the merry migrants come to brighten her day, 'this way'.

Gaia followed the old packhorse route that crossed the surrounding wasteland and traversed the muddy marsh found herself at the canal by lunchtime, teenager now, she sat on a coppiced hazel stool and looked for the Sun in a slow greening meadow, imagined him walking towards her through the stubble field where the new estate was marked, a gyre of grey geese gathering at his feet and the sky above his head no longer the scar of jet trails but the soft silk twitch of skylarks and curlews announcing his arrival on the thermal pull.

The touch of new life, she imagined the only reason for his crossing the celestial equinox was to find her hoped the chain around her neck still sparkled, daisy bright, the buttercup earrings she wore in her ears threaded to help her see clearly if she needed them in the night.

The afternoon she spent following the dry-stone wall and the standing stones, her hands on the moss covered rock she noticed the ruins of past lives those that had deified his light, stopping to admire the hawthorn that cast colour over the parapet, the lonely faces that stared from windows their cheeks stained with the sweet, pink blossom.

Late afternoon Gaia was determined to fall in love, she looked for signs beneath the hedgerows the way daisies crouched low and held hands with the snowdrops a little dance to warm them in preparation for something to come. Time interrupted, time out of place, place out of time and the gift of flowers to carry her through a cooler hour, a blanket made of pink and white corolla to surround her. Head heavy heart like a drum and still she continued to ask, where is the Sun?

When she came to the river she walked its slippery banks, the lagan waters that ran toward the waiting sea and wondered which coast was east? They said if he was coming that was where he'd be moving through, the spring bloom a moment of alluring magic unfurling in the dusky gloom. Light lifting and yet the clouds still confused her, the only hint of heat the wild display of lightbulbs that lit up her feet, the daffodils that asked her to trust them, her curious fingers dipped and dyed by their yokes, small suns, tiny tracing footsteps, this way. At Gaia's ankles the tangled tapestry of new shoots and against her hands the crumpled leaves still clinging to stubborn oak and the red-tailed bumblebee circling calling her over asking her to follow, head to the blackthorn to watch it shed its white dress, a gift of satin and silk fallen onto the young women's shoulders, no weight at all.

Here, warmth, no matter how fleeting, the setting Sun glimpsed briefly through the budding trees enough for Gaia to hold on, lift a little of him into her pockets some heat stored beneath her tea-cosy hat, she told him he was coming home with her that he was needed to bring hope to those who needed to believe in hope.

Together they left the river and returned home through a gap in the pennywort wall, past the daisy hedgerows and the canal, the silenced railways and motorways no matter how his heat lessened his colour lifted kissed her home horizon like he knew it, loved it. He told her tonight he had to be somewhere else but she made him promise, tomorrow he would rise early gift them with better light so they might see a way through, he'd shine it into the corners never before noticed lift all the small things into Gaia's hands the gift of her would be enough.

The Sun left her standing in the park, no tea-time children playing on the swings but Mother Nature knew they would again and soon, she imagined the tables and chairs pulled from kitchens and petal bunting hung in the trees, allotment grown food cooked and homebrew drunk and splashed from inch-full paddling pools, the frogs and the kids and all the visiting birds come down to celebrate and her own stomach full of new life to breathe in the win of light over dark, the sound of hope's heart beating out the movement of her own little secret thing, for now, rebirth.

ACKNOWLEDGEMENTS

First and foremost I would like to thank fellow working class hero, Linda Cleary, who, as Editor and Publishing Lead at Hypatia Publications, could see how important the telling of these stories was. Without her passion and vision this book wouldn't have been possible.

Acknowledgements are also due to Literature Works and the Canal & River Trust who commissioned me to write *River Running Over* as part of my writer residency at Custom House Exeter 2020. Thanks also to the National Trust for commissioning me to write a creative essay by interpreting the writings of nature lovers all over the UK who took part in the Spring Nature Diary project 2020 - that piece became *Hope's Heart Beats*.

ABOUT

Natasha Carthew is a working class Writer and Performance Poet from Cornwall. She has written two books of poetry, three acclaimed Young Adult novels; *Winter Damage*, *The Light That Gets Lost* and *Only the Ocean* published with Bloomsbury and her latest Adult literary fiction *All Rivers Run Free* published by Quercus Books. Her new prose-poem *Song for the Forgotten* published with National Trust Books in 2020 and her latest short story features in *HAG: Forgotten Folk Tales* published by Virago Press in October 2020. 2021 sees the publication of *Born Between Crosses,* a new sequence of prose-poetry celebrating the working lives of rural working class women published by Hypatia Publications.

Natasha has written extensively on the subject of what it means to be a working class writer and how authentic working class voices are represented in fiction for several publications and programmes; including Writers' & Artists' Yearbook, The Royal Society of Authors Journal, BBC Radio 3, BBC Radio 4, The Guardian, Dark Mountain Project, The Herald, The Bookseller, Book Brunch and The Big Issue.

Natasha is the Founder and Artistic Director of The Working Class Writers Festival - in partnership with The Festival of Ideas and sponsored by Hachette UK and Penguin Random House.

MORE FROM HYPATIA PUBLICATIONS

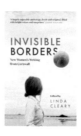

Invisible Borders. New Women's Writing from Cornwall
£10.50
ISBN: 978-1-872229-67-6
Print length: 84 pages
Edited by Linda Cleary
Published by Hypatia Publications September 2020

Invisible Borders. New Women's Writing from Cornwall is a collection of writing from 23 women writers with poetry and stories that take you on a journey through Cornwall and beyond, inspired by this westernmost wilderness and its coastline, whilst also reaching outward to cities and places far from its shores in a rich map of fresh writing.

Featuring the work of: Jacky Garratt, Vivienne Tregenza, Benigale Richards, Laura Sennen, Lucia Johns, Mary Charnley, Faye Wilson, Diana Dixon, Jude Brickhill, Rupam Baoni, Vicki Morley, Mary Oliver, Lou Sarabadzic, Katrina Naomi, Penelope Shuttle, Abigail Elizabeth Ottley, Alice Kavounas, Pascale Petit, Natasha Carthew, Katherine Stansfield, Linda Cleary, Lesley Hale and Ella Frears.

Also available as an eBook and audiobook. Available with other titles in the online bookshop:
https://hypatia-trust.org.uk/bookshop